Printed in the United States of America

First Printing, 2021

ISBN 978-1-954829-01-5

Lynette Smith

Cover design by Lynette Smith

Dedication

TO GOD WHO IS THE HEAD OF MY LIFE. I COULD
NOT HAVE GOTTEN THROUGH ANYTHING
WITHOUT HIM.

TO MY BEAUTIFUL CHILDREN JAMIA AND JJ, I
LOVE YOU MORE THAN ANYTHING AND SO
BLESSED AND HONORED TO BE YOUR MOM.
THANK YOU FOR BEING MY INSPIRATION.

TO MY MOMMY AND DADDY, I TRULY DEDICATE
THIS BOOK TO YOU FOR ALWAYS BEING SO
SUPPORTING AND LOVING.

LAST BUT NEVER LEAST I DEDICATE THIS BOOK
TO MY FAMILY, FRIENDS, SISTERS IN POWER,
GIRLS TOO WOMEN INC. AND BOYS TOO MEN INC.
YOU GAVE ME THE COURAGE TO SPEAK OUT
LOUD ABOUT MY DEPRESSION AND ANXIETY BUT
MOST OF ALL TO ALLOW MY STORY TO BECOME A
TESTIMONY...

CONTENT

INTRODUCTION

WELCOME TO TOGETHER WE ARE ONE

FOUNDER/EXECUTIVE DIRECTOR LYNETTE SMITH

Hello, my name is Lynette Smith. In 2001 I was diagnosed with Bipolar Disorder. As a child, I suffered from low self-esteem as a result of being bullied. Depression, low self-esteem and anxiety followed me throughout childhood and into adulthood. It seemed like I couldn't get away from it no matter how hard I tried. For many years, I felt like there was this dark cloud following me everywhere, making it impossible for me to truly live my life. My depression was severe, it had an effect on every part of my life. My spirits were so low, that I often found it hard to even interact with people the way that I wanted to. I had several dreams and aspirations but I could not find the strength to even try to achieve them.

In December 2016 after reading my daughter's diary, I decided that I needed to make life altering changes. She wrote that she thought that I was in the bed dead because I hadn't moved all day long. I was in a deep sleep as a result of being prescribed a daily dose of 600 mg of Seroquel. She stated that she was very scared and that she didn't want to lose her Mommy. That day I made a decision that would change my life. I began to live and love myself more and more each day.

In the chapters that follow you will learn many things about mental health and the tremendous effect that it can have on your life. You will also learn about different mental health conditions, coping skills and the regiment that I use to help keep my mental health intact.

Chapter

1

What is Mental Health/Illness?

What is Mental Health?

Mental health encompasses emotional, psychological and social well-being. It has a profound effect on how we respond to stress, relate to others and even on our decision making abilities. The state of our mental health can be affected by a number of factors including environmental, biological and socio economic. Maintaining our mental health is important at every age and stage of our lives because our mental health is essential to our overall health. Peak mental health allows a person to realize their full potential, cope with the stresses of life and be productive.

What is Mental Illness?

A mental illness is a condition that impacts a person's feelings, behavior or mood. These conditions can impact a person's daily living and personal relationships. When suffering from mental illness, many people tend to feel isolated and alone. I want you to know that you are NOT alone.

As you progress through this workbook you will learn more about mental health and some common mental health disorders. You will also complete different activities that will introduce coping skills that have helped me along the way.

- 1 in 20 US adults experience serious mental illness each year
- 1 in 6 US youth age 6-17 experience a mental health disorder each year
- 50% of all lifetime mental illness begins by age 14, and 75% by age 24
- Suicide is the 2nd leading cause of death among people age 10-34

We all have a darkside at some time in our life, some of us are better at masking and dealing with it than others.

I was feeling very depressed with low self-esteem and feeling pain from the inside out. But most of all I was feeling very ALONE.

APRIL 2019

I learned to live with my Bipolar Disorder by practicing my coping skills. Most of all I have learned to "Love Me" while living with a mental illness

December 2020

Chapter

2

Why is Mental Health so important?

<u>*Why is your Mental Health So Important?*</u>

Mental health is important because it is a critical component to your physical well being. If your body is worn out and you are not resting or taking the time to clear your mind it makes it really hard to focus.

When we are doing well physically, we are able to exercise, eat healthy and allow our minds to be free. The ability to think clearly and focus allows you to adapt to most changes and cope with all of the adversities that may come your way.

There are some things that you can do that will help you maintain good mental health. These work for me to this day. Below you will find a list of a few of my favorite things to do to help keep my mental health in good standing.

1. Sleep - It is especially important to get a good night's rest. It gives your mind the time it needs to wind down. When you are stressed, your mind seems to be running 90 miles per minute. This is when insomnia enters the picture and takes over. Insomnia increases stress and can physically wear your body down. Getting eight hours of sleep each night is ideal.

2. Exercise- Exercising is important. Physical workouts helped me to stay focused. Finding a workout partner helped to keep me accountable and receive the support that I needed to keep going. It's good to work out and have someone to talk to.

3. Going for a walk- Getting outside for a walk around the neighborhood, park or even sitting outside with your pet can be very therapeutic. It helps you to relax, relate and release. This is really one of my favorites.

There are a lot more things that you can do to keep your mental health in shape. I hope that my favorites can help you as much as they have helped me.

Chapter
3

Mental Health Conditions

Bipolar Disorder

Bipolar disorder is associated with episodes of mood swings that range from the lows of depression to the highs of mania. The exact cause of bipolar disorder is not known. It effects you moods sometimes where you feel very low one minute and the next minute your fine.

Manic episodes include symptoms such as a sudden increase in energy, a reduced need for sleep and loss of touch with reality. There are also physical symptoms that can include chest pain and shortness of breath.

Depressive episodes include symptoms such as low energy, loss of motivation and interest in daily activities. These episodes also include feelings of sadness, hopelessness and anxiety.

For me my Mood episodes lasted for weeks to months at a time . It has been known to also increase suicidal thoughts.

Bipolar disorder can be a lifelong illness. Getting treatment typically involves a combination of medication and therapy.

Anxiety Disorder

A mental health disorder that is characterized by overwhelming feelings of worry, distress or fear that are intense enough to disrupt one's daily activities.

Examples of anxiety disorders include:

- Generalized Anxiety Disorder
- Panic Disorder,
- Obsessive-Compulsive Disorder (OCD)
- Social Anxiety and
- Post-Traumatic Stress Disorder (PTSD)

Symptoms include feeling intense impending danger or doom, inability to set aside a worry, increased heart rate, hyperventilation, trembling and restlessness. Treatment includes psychological counseling or medications, including antidepressants.

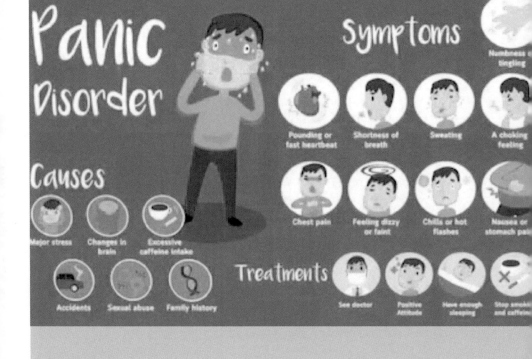

Post Traumatic Stress Disorder

PTSD is a mental health condition that is characterized by intense, disturbing thoughts and feelings related to past trauma. The condition may be triggered long after the trauma is experienced.

Symptoms may include nightmares or intrusive memories,, distress to reminders of the trauma, heightened reactions, anxiety, or depressed mood. Physical symptoms include pain, nausea, sweating and trembling. Symptoms may begin within three months of the experienced trauma, but sometimes may take years to begin.

Cognitive Behavioral Therapy has consistently been found to tbe the most effective treatment for PTSD.

Some of us have experienced trauma in our lives that is so significant that we keep reliving it over and over. It often feels like the past is haunting you. Getting therapy can truly help in this area because we are able to talk about what we we are experiencing. Most of all we find a way to deal with it so we are able to move forward.

<u>*Schizophrenia*</u>

A serious mental disorder that typically involves psychosis where people may experience a loss of connection with reality. It affects how a person thinks, feels and behaves.

Schizophrenia is characterized by hallucinations, delusions, disordered thinking and behavior, including hearing voices and paranoia.

Treatment is usually lifelong and often involves a combination of medications, psychotherapy and coordinated social services.

Living with Schizophrenia can really be tricky and dangerous. Many times those who are affected may see or hear things that are not really there. That's why its good to take your medicine and continue therapy to keep your thoughts and actions in good standing.

Major Depression

A mood disorder characterized by persistent sadness or loss of interest in activities, causing significant impairment in daily life. Sometimes it can make you feel like life isn't worth living. Possible causes include a combination of biological, psychological, and social sources of distress.

Aside from sadness and loss of interest symptoms may include changes in sleep, appetite, energy level, concentration, daily behavior, and self-esteem. Depression can also be associated with thoughts of suicide.

The mainstay of treatment is usually medication, talk therapy, or a combination of the two. Increasingly, research suggests these treatments may normalize brain changes associated with depression.

Borderline Personality Disorder

Borderline Personality Disorder (BPD) is a condition characterized by ongoing patterns of varying moods, self-image and behavior that is often known to co-exist with other disorders. This means that people who experience BPD feel emotions intensely and for extended periods of time, and it is harder for them to return to a stable mood after an emotionally triggering event.

Symptoms include mood swings and altered self image. Other signs may include unstable relationships, impulsive often dangerous behavior, self harm, recurring thoughts of suicide and feelings of emptiness, among others. The severity and frequency of symptoms vary depending on the individual.

Statics state that 1.6% of the adult U.S. population experiences BPD. Nearly 75% of people diagnosed with BPD are women. Recent research suggests that men may be equally affected by BPD, but are commonly misdiagnosed with PTSD or depression.

Unstable relationships

Impulsive, self-destructive behaviors

B orderline

Feeling suspicious or out of touch with reality

Explosive anger

P ersonality

Self harm

Unclear of shifting self-image

D isorder

Extreme emotional swings

Fear of abandonment

Chronic feelings of emptiness

22

Eating Disorders

Eating disorders are one of the most common conditions. These disorders are characterized by persistent eating behavior that have a negative impact on your health, emotions and ability to function in certain areas of life.

Many people become so consumed with food and weight issues that they struggle to focus on life. It may be an early sign of an eating disorder.

Without treatment, eating disorders can take over a person's life and lead to serious health concerns, which may also can lead to deadly medical complications. Eating disorders can affect both adults and children. This disorder can cause conditions that cause serious emotional and physical problems which will also include weight gain.

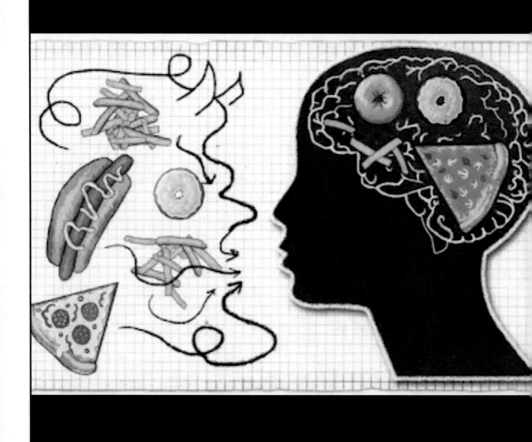

Chapter
4

Symptoms of Mental Health

Signs/Symptoms

You may or may not be familiar with the various signs and symptoms of mental health concerns.

Below I have listed 14 signs and symptoms for you to study and be able to recognize if you or someone you know is experiencing them.

1.Feeling sad or down

2.Confused thinking or reduced ability to concentrate

3. Excessive fears or worries, or extreme feelings of guilt

4.Extreme mood changes of highs and lows

5.Withdrawal from family, friends and activities

6.Significant tiredness, low energy or problems sleeping

7.Experiencing (delusions), paranoia or hallucinations

8.Inability to cope with daily problems or stress

Signs/Symptoms

9.Trouble understanding and relating to situations and to people

10. Problems with alcohol or drug use

11. Major changes in eating habits

12. Changes in sex drive

13. Excessive anger, hostility or violence

14. Suicidal thoughts

15. Loss of interest or pleasure in your activities

16. Weight loss or gain

17. Trouble getting to sleep or feeling sleepy during the day

18. Feelings restless and agitated.

19. Very sluggish and slowed down physically or mentally

20 .Being tired and without energy

21. Feeling worthless or guilty

Signs/Symptoms

22. Trouble concentrating or making decisions

23. Thoughts of suicide

24. A decrease in energy

25. Feelings of helplessness or hopelessness

26. Feeling confused, forgetful, angry, nervous, or on edge

27. An inability to do daily tasks

28. Severe mood swings

29. Thoughts of self-harm

OUR MENTAL HEALTH

IS JUST AS IMPORTANT AS

OUR PHYSICAL HEALTH

Chapter

5

Coping Skills for Mental Health

Coping Skills

1. _Start (and Stay) Active_ Being overwhelmed and tired will decrease your motivation. Try to exercise as often as you can. Now I have to tell up front it will be difficult at first. But know that "YOU CAN DO THIS". Take it slow. Even 10 minutes of exercise can help your mood. Gradually add more time and exercise as time goes on. At this point you will began enjoying your work out. Now your ready to implement a workout schedule. It's not about how much you do, but maintaining a schedule. Then you will notice your mood changing and your spirit improving.

2. For those who have a special _belief_ or a religion this is for you. Believing in something is the glue that holds us together and can give us the power to move forward during challenging times. Now let me say this, it doesn't fix the problem but at times can help.

3. _Eating a Balanced Meal_ helps a lot . We hear it all the time from our doctor, that changing our eating habits can be a critical component of a depression. But drastic changes may harm you. I would suggest make the change as if you are on a weight loss journey. Gradually decrease bad foods for healthy ones. You will also notice when doing that, your energy level will begin to increase as well.

<u>Coping Skills</u>

4. *Setting a weekly goal*. Setting a goal not only allows you to accomplish things but also gives you something to look forward to. Again don't move too fast, take one step at a time. I would start with one goal per week. Start with a simple goal like going for a 30 minute walk everyday or writing your feelings down everyday. All of these goals are exercises that will increase your moods. After while you will realize you are now having more positive days.

5. *Journaling*. This one of my favorites. START YOU A JOURNAL. When dealing with mental health, there is huge stigma around it because so many are scared of speaking up and out about suffering. It then becomes silently embedded that turns into internal poison. This has been done so much because we are judge a lot about our feelings and what we are experiencing. With Journaling you are able to write down all of your thoughts and feelings with out judgement. I use this mechansim so often because IT WORKS! It allows me to be free with my pen while releasing the silent voice inside me.

Coping Skills

6. *Positive Affirmations*. One thing i have noticed during my journey of Mental Health, that speaking positivity out loud helps instill in me " I AM ENOUGH" You can write down 3 positive affirmations daily to recite to your self in the mirror. After reciting them daily watch the transformation. Ok lets go, I will start you off. Go to you mirror. Face your Mirror and say; " I AM BEAUTIFUL" I AM STRONG" I AM MORE THAN ENOUGH". See doesnt that feel good?

7. Staying in touch with close family and friends. Form a circle for support. (i.e. family/friends, counselors, psychiatrists, or support groups)

8. Deep breathing exercises. It helps to think positive thoughts while breathing in and out. It helped me to stay relaxed.

9. Listen to music. I love listening to gospel or my church music. Music allows me to take my mind off my anxiety and go into a spiritual place to help my thoughts. Find whatever music that you enjoy and use it.

10. Meditation. Meditating will help your mind from racing. It helped calm my thoughts. It allows me to keep positive thoughts.

<u>*Coping Skills*</u>

11. *Avoiding caffeinated beverages.* This helped me a lot because caffeine can get your adrenaline running really high sometimes. Avoiding certain foods and drinks helps a lot with anxiety.

There are many different coping skills you can use to help manage your mental health. The key is finding the ones that works for you and using them whenever your mental health is compromised or on the verge of being so.

Conclusion

In conclusion, I hope this Mental Health Workbook Guide will help you as much as it has helped me. Being able to share some information about Mental Health and some of the skills that help me , hopefully will now help you on your new journey. Today is a New Day! Always know that" Mental Health is just as important as our Physical Health". Always take time to take care of you. It starts with you and "YOU CAN DO THIS"

ACTIVITY #1

1 - Describe your self using two words?

2 - Why do you feel these two words describe you?

ACTIVITY #2

Answer the questions below and make a list of the next steps you will take once making the change.

What do you need to do to increase positive moods.

What changes do I think needs to be made?	How I will make the change	How I will stay motivated

Out your answer to the question below:

_____
_____
_____
_____
_____

Checklist for next steps.

1.
2.
3.
4.

5.
6.
7.
8.

ACTIVITY #3

On this Activity you will Answer these questions.
List what makes you Happy? Like things you love
to do, places you like to go and more. Then tell me
what makes you sad. Things you don't like, What
makes those sad feelings surface and why you feel
that way., .

WHAT MAKES YOU HAPPY?

WHAT MAKES YOU SAD?

Name 3 of your greatest strengths and why are those your greatest strengths?

ACTIVITY #4

In this Activity list all negative people/things that needs to be removed.. By doing this you will be cleaning out your inner closet. Its like throwing out clothes and shoes you don't use anymore. Except you will be throwing out Negative people, Thoughts and Actions.

Removing Negativity #1

Removing Negativity #2

Removing Negativity #3

ACTIVITY #5

In this Activity, I want you to think about all of the coping mechanisms that you have learned thus far to complete this task. List what and how your life will be months and years from now.

A- 3 MONTHS

D - 2 YEARS

B - 6 MONTHS

E - 5 YEARS

C - 1 YEAR

F - 10 YEARS

DAILY AFFIRMATION

Everyday you will take 10 minutes out of your day to go to your mirror and recite your Daily Affirmations I have listed below;

STEP 1
"I AM STRONG"

STEP 2
"I AM BEAUTIFUL"

STEP 3
"I CAN DO THIS"

STEP 4
"I AM MORE THAN ENOUGH"

STEP 5
"TODAY IS A NEW DAY"

WEEKLY GOALS

MONDAY

TUESDAY

WEDNESDAY

THURSDAY

FRIDAY

WEEKEND

WWW.GIRLSTOOWOMENINC.COM

WEEKLY GOALS

MONDAY

TUESDAY

WEDNESDAY

THURSDAY

FRIDAY

WEEKEND

WEEKLY GOALS

MONDAY

TUESDAY

WEDNESDAY

THURSDAY

FRIDAY

WEEKEND

WWW.GIRLSTOOWOMENINC.COM

WEEKLY GOALS

MONDAY

TUESDAY

WEDNESDAY

THURSDAY

FRIDAY

WEEKEND

NOTES/JOURNAL

NOTES/JOURNAL

NOTES/JOURNAL

NOTES/JOURNAL

NOTES/JOURNAL

NOTES/JOURNAL

NOTES/JOURNAL

NOTES/JOURNAL

NOTES/JOURNAL

NOTES/JOURNAL

NOTES/JOURNAL

NOTES/JOURNAL

NOTES/JOURNAL

NOTES/JOURNAL

NOTES/JOURNAL

NOTES/JOURNAL

NOTES/JOURNAL

NOTES/JOURNAL

NOTES/JOURNAL

NOTES/JOURNAL

NOTES/JOURNAL

NOTES/JOURNAL

NOTES/JOURNAL

NOTES/JOURNAL

NOTES/JOURNAL

NOTES/JOURNAL

NOTES/JOURNAL

NOTES/JOURNAL

NOTES/JOURNAL

NOTES/JOURNAL

NOTES/JOURNAL

NOTES/JOURNAL

NOTES/JOURNAL

NOTES/JOURNAL

NOTES/JOURNAL

NOTES/JOURNAL

NOTES/JOURNAL

RESOURCES LIST

1

National Alliance of Mental Illness

Suicide Prevention Lifeline. (800) 273-TALK or (800) SUICIDE. NAMI Information Line. (800) 950-NAMI.

2

National Suicide Prevention Lifeline

1-800-273-8255

3

Hope Line

CALL OR TEXT: 919-231-4525 | 877-235-4525

4

NCDHHS

IF YOU HAVE ANY FURTHER QUESTIONS REGARDING CRISIS SERVICES WITHIN NC, PLEASE CONTACT 984-236-5300, OR 800-662-7030 FOR SPANISH

Made in the USA
Middletown, DE
25 April 2021